CW00350899

SPRING HARVEST
P R A I S E

One for All

SONGBOOK

60 SONGS FOR THE CHURCH
WITH FULL SCORES

COPYRIGHT & PHOTOCOPYING

No part of this publication may be reproduced in any form without the permission of the copyright holder of the songs and the publisher of the songbook. Exceptions to this rule are made for holders of licences issued by Christian Copyright Licensing International, as follows:

CHURCH COPYRIGHT LICENCE/COLLECTIVE WORSHIP COPYRIGHT LICENCE:
Churches, schools and organisations holding a church or collective worship copyright licence may reproduce and store the words of the songs within the terms of their licence.

MUSIC REPRODUCTION LICENCE/COLLECTIVE WORSHIP MUSIC REPRODUCTION LICENCE:
Churches, schools and organisations holding a music reproduction licence may photocopy the words and/or music of the songs directly from this publication within the terms of their licence.

For information about these licences visit www.ccli.co.uk.

FOR UK, IRELAND AND EUROPE:
Christian Copyright Licensing International Ltd
Chantry House, 22 Upperton Road, Eastbourne,
East Sussex, BN21 1BF
www.ccli.co.uk

FOR ASIA PACIFIC:
Christian Copyright Licensing International
PO Box 6644, Baulkham Hills BC,
NSW 2153 Australia
www.ccli.com.au

FOR USA AND CANADA:
Christian Copyright Licensing Inc,
17201 NE Sacramento Street, Portland,
Oregon, 97230 USA
www.ccli.com

FOR AFRICA:
Christian Copyright Licensing Africa (Pty) Ltd,
PO Box 2347, Durbanville 7551, South Africa
www.ccli.co.za

FOR BRAZIL:
CCLI LICENCIAMENTO DE DIREITOS AUTORAIS Ltda.
Alameda Rio Negro, 1084 - Sala 75
CEP 06454-000 Barueri, SP Brasil
www.ccli.com.br

KEEPING WITHIN THE LAW
If your church musicians play direct from hymnbooks, such as this one, then the purchase price of each book pays the royalties due to copyright owners. However, if you wish to photocopy music for your musicians then you will normally need permission from the copyright owner(s). Alternatively you can obtain a Music Reproduction Licence* from CCLI which permits you to photocopy the words and music of hymns and worship songs from authorised** music publications. This licence also permits you to make customised musical arrangements for transposing instruments such as wind and brass provided the melody line remains unchanged.

* The Music Reproduction Licence is supplementary to the Church Copyright Licence, i.e. your church must hold both licences.

** An Authorised book is one which is covered by the Music Reproduction Licence. NB: Both the publication containing the song you wish to photocopy and the song itself must be covered by the Music Reproduction Licence.

For more information, contact CCLI on +44 (0)1323 436103 or visit www.ccli.co.uk.

UNAUTHORISED PHOTOCOPYING IS ILLEGAL and detrimental to the work and ministry of the songwriters and publishers.

All rights reserved. All songs are reproduced by kind permission of the copyright holders – names of which are shown below each song/hymn. Any omission of acknowledgement to composer or publisher will be corrected in future editions.

ACKNOWLEDGEMENTS

Music type-setting for scores and lead sheets: David Ball
Guitar chords: David Ball
Artwork: Sublime | wearesublime.com
Executive Producer: Peter Martin

Special thanks to Brenda Cameron and all at Cambron Software for Power Music and your help in developing this resource.

Spring Harvest wishes to acknowledge and thank the following people for their help in the compilation and production of this songbook: Denise Anstead, Pete Broadbent, Andrew Crookall, Cheryl Jenkinson, Sue Rinaldi & Rachel Whitney.

Published & distributed by Essential Christian, 14 Horsted Square, Uckfield, East Sussex, TN22 1QG, UK. Registered Charity number 1126997.

All Scripture quotations unless indicated otherwise taken from THE HOLY BIBLE, NEW INTERNATIONAL VERSION®, NIV®. Copyright © 1973, 1978, 1984, 2011 by Biblica, Inc.® Used by permission. All rights reserved worldwide.

All copyright details correct at time of going to press.

ISBN 978-1-911237-04-4

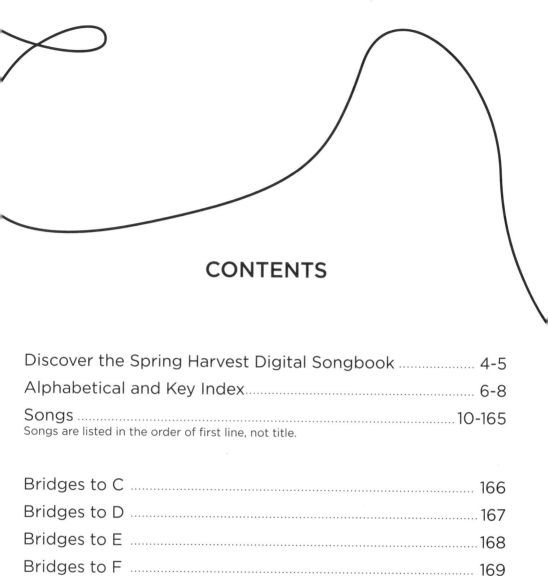

CONTENTS

DISCOVER THE SPRING HARVEST DIGITAL SONGBOOK

Over the years of the Spring Harvest Songbook, we have always been looking at how we can use technology to make worship leaders' lives easier and make the flow of worship smoother. Power Music from Cambron Software has been at the heart of our digital songbooks since 2011 and is widely used by worship musicians to free themselves from the hassles of paper music. In Power Music all your music is instantly available on-screen for practice and performance.

Once again we have worked in partnership with Cambron Software to create a digital version of the Spring Harvest 2017 Songbook. This includes sheet music, chord sheets, lyrics and all the indexing required to find your songs quickly.

Use your iPad, PC, laptop, Windows tablet or Mac as a "digital" music stand to display music or chord sheets on-screen.

WHY USE POWER MUSIC?

 Songs are easy to find by title, first line, category, author and Bible reference

 Quickly set up playlists for your services

 Transpose chord sheets, add capo chords

 Add performance notes

 Link audio tracks for practice or performance.

 Using multiple screens keeps the whole band on the same page

 Synchronised iPad display

 Page turning becomes simple using a foot pedal or by simply tapping a screen or a keyboard.

No more searching for scraps of paper, no more filing song sheets, no more photocopying - Power Music makes worship times stress free for musicians.

One *for* All
SONGBOOK

iPAD

Get Spring Harvest 2017 Songbook on your iPad using the free Power Music app.

DOWNLOAD* (Windows & Mac OS X)

- Display sheet music and chord sheets
- Transpose chord sheets
- Search by title, author, category, Bible reference

Find your unique reference code on the inside front cover

HELP*

Getting started

*See inside front cover for details

ALPHABETICAL INDEX

[Song titles differing from first lines are in italics]

SPRING
HARVEST
2017

ALL I HAVE BECAUSE
OF JESUS
(I WILL BOAST IN CHRIST)

Key = D

Reuben Morgan & Scott Ligertwood

Copyright © 2016 Hillsong Music Publishing
publishing@hillsong.com

CCLI # 7068427

11

D.S. al Coda

I will

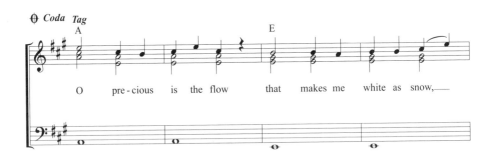

Coda **Tag**

O pre-cious is the flow that makes me white as snow,——

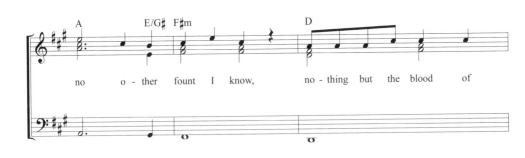

no o-ther fount I know, no-thing but the blood of

Je - sus. No-thing but the blood of Je - sus.

AMAZING GRACE

Words: John Newton & Colin Webster

Intro: (see.) (ry.) (lieved.)

1. A-
2. Twas
3. The

Verse

1. maz - ing grace, how sweet the sound that saved a wretch like me. I
2. grace that taught my heart to fear and grace my fears re - lieved. How
3. Lord has pro - mised good to me, His Word my hope se - cures; He

1. once was lost but now am found, was blind but now I
2. pre - cious did that grace ap - pear the
3. will my shield and por - tion be as

hour I first be - long as life en

Chorus

lieved. 1. A - maz - ing grace, I stand in awe, that Christ should die for
dures. 2. Through ma - ny dan - gers toils and snares I have al - rea - dy

13

Copyright © 2016 Colin Webster Songs
(Adm Song Solutions www.songsolutions.org)

CCLI# 7057564

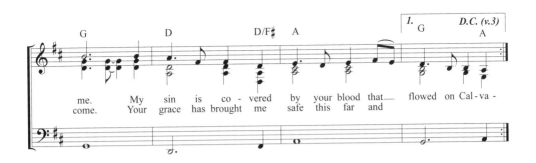

me. My sin is co-vered by your blood that flowed on Cal-va-

come. Your grace has brought me safe this far and

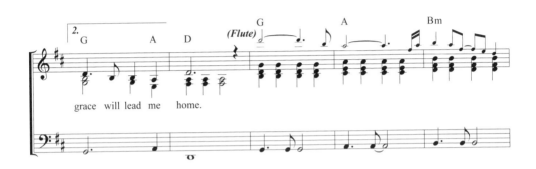

grace will lead me home.

4. When we've been there ten thou-sand years, bright shin-ing as the

sun; we've no less days to sing God's praise than— when we first be-

gun. 3. All glo-ry be to God on high, all ho-nour and all praise. We'll

sing with those who dwell a-bove, saved— by a-maz-ing grace. All

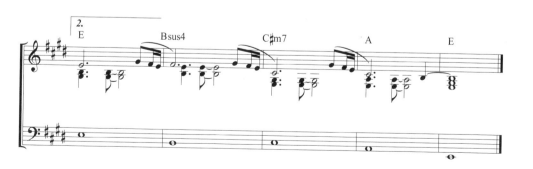

ARE YOU THIRSTY?
(LIVING WATERS)

Key = C

Ed Cash & Kristyn Getty

♩ = 84

Verse

1. Are you thir-sty? Are you emp-ty?___ Come and drink these liv-ing
2. Christ is call-ing, find re - fresh-ing___ at the cross of liv-ing
3. Spi - rit mov-ing, mer - cy wash-ing,___ heal - ing in these liv-ing
4. Are you thir-sty? Are you emp-ty?___ Come and drink these liv-ing

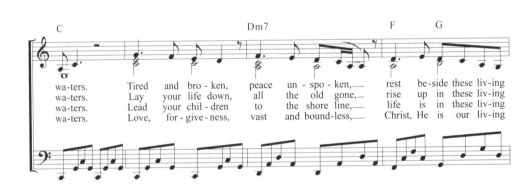

wa-ters. Tired and bro-ken, peace un-spo-ken,___ rest be-side these liv-ing
wa-ters. Lay your life down, all the old gone,___ rise up in these liv-ing
wa-ters. Lead your chil-dren to the shore line,___ life is in these liv-ing
wa-ters. Love, for-give-ness, vast and bound-less,___ Christ, He is our liv-ing

1.,4. **2nd time jump to Chorus** **2.,3.** **Chorus**

wa-ters. There's a wa-ters. There's a ri - ver_ that flows with

Copyright © 2016 Getty Music Publishing/Alletrop Music
(Adm Music Services/Song Solutions www.songsolutions.org)

CCLI # 7063743

mer-cy and love, bring-ing joy to the cit-y of our God.   There our hope is se-cure, do not

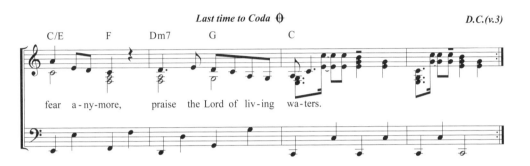

Last time to Coda Ⓗ   *D.C.(v.3)*

fear a-ny-more,   praise the Lord of liv-ing wa-ters.

Bridge

Oo,——   oo,——   oo,——   oo.   oo.

Ⓗ *Coda*

wa-ters. There our hope is se-cure, do not fear a-ny-more, praise the Lord of liv-ing wa-ters.

4

BEHOLD THIS KING
SO INNOCENT
(ONCE FOR ALL)

Key = G

Paul Baloche, Matt Redman
& Jorge Mhondera

♩ = 70

1. Be-hold this King, so in - no - cent, a crown of
   love can still be seen, on your
   sha - dow of the cross, we see our

thorns up - on his head; feel his heart, his heart of grace. Be-hold this
hands and on your feet; we feel your heart, your heart of grace. Hea - ven's
shame for what it was, and feel your heart, your heart of grace. We see your

Man of suf - fer - ing, who bore the cross and all our shame; breathe a-
gates have o - pened wide, You have raised us up to life; we breathe a-
po - wer break - ing through, and all that we've be - come in you; we breathe a-

gain, this my - ste - ry.
gain, this my - ste - ry.
gain, this my - ste - ry.

Pre-Chorus Em

1. Nailed to a cross, there in our
2. Up from the grave, now raised to

18

Copyright © 2016 Thankyou Music/Said and Done Music (Adm. by CapitolCMGPublishing.com excl. UK & Europe,
adm. by Integrity Music, part of the David C Cook family, songs@integritymusic.com)/ Leadworship Songs/
Integrity Worship Music/sixsteps Music (Adm. by CapitolCMGPublishing.com excl. UK,
adm. by Integrity Music, part of the David C Cook family, songs@integritymusic.com)

CCLI# 7067214

place, O Lamb of God, you made a way. Once for
life, O Son of God, we lift you high.

all you died so I could live a-gain. Once for all you washed a-way our

— sin. Streams of mer-cy and love flow-ing free for-e-ver-more. And your

Last time to Coda **1.**   **D.C.(v.2)**

blood ran down once for all. 2. The scars of

THIS SONG IS FEATURED ON **NEWSONGS FOR THE CHURCH 2017**

BY GRACE I HAVE BEEN SAVED
(GRACE (WIDE AS THE OCEAN))

Key = D

Harvey Jessop, Pete James
& Charles Austin Miles

1. By grace I have been saved; new mer-cies rise with each new
-day and through the years, you've shared my joys and dried my
know for all my days, through seas of calm or fier-cest

day. Through the night in God's em-brace, I'm wrapped in love and held by
tears. When my love ebbs like the tide, flood-gates of grace fling o - pen
waves bound-less grace for e - ver-more will guide me to e - ter-nal

__ grace.
__ wide.
__shores.

2. To -

Wide, wide as the o-

-cean, high as the hea - vens a - bove,__ deep, deep as the deep-

Copyright © Harvey Jessop & Pete James

21

CCLI# 7056552

6

CAN I WALK THE PATH LESS TRODDEN?
(HIGHWAY TO THE HEAVENS)

Key = F

Capo 3 (G)

♩ = 72

Cathy Burton

1. Can I walk the path less trod-den, in-to the se-cret place? where I can glimpse your face.
2. Let me walk be-side still wa-ters, and then dive in-to the deep; the trea-sure that I seek.
3. Let me walk each step be-side you, let your Spi-rit flood my heart, all my dreams and all my scars.

find the high-way to the hea-vens,
Je-sus, lead me to di-sco-ver
let the o-ver-flow wash o-ver

God un-chang-ing, e-ver faith-ful, Lord e-ter-nal, King of love; here I

Copyright © 2016 Song Solutions
www.songsolutions.org

24

CCLI# 7071711

25

12 NEW SONGS TO INSPIRE THE CHURCH TO WORSHIP

Hear a selection of new songs written by a variety of leading songwriters. It's a wonderful resource for personal devotion or can be used as a resource for worship teams.

All 12 songs are featured in the songbook!

Available at essential⟨ ⟩n Bookshops

7

CHRIST WAS RAISED

Key = E

Sam Hargreaves

𝅘𝅥 = 110

1. Christ was raised, e - ven death could not con - tain him, we are
raised, the re - stor - er of cre - a - tion, by his

saved, Sa - tan's pow'r he o - ver - came; no more shame, no more guilt and con - dem -
grace mak - ing earth and hea - ven new. We are changed, a - gents of his re - cre -

na - tion, in his name, in his name. Christ is
a - tion in all we do, all we do. Christ is

raised, he is seat - ed with the Fa - ther, and the Spi - rit that raised him gives us
raised, so our strug - gles have a pur - pose, he's a - live, so our work is not in
raised, with a new and glo - rious bo - dy, scars of love in his hands and in his

life; so we'll live to the glo - ry of our Sa - viour, hal - le -
vain; and we'll serve for the glo - ry of our Sa - viour, hal - le -
side. So we'll sing to the glo - ry of our Sa - viour, hal - le -

Words & music: © Sam Hargreaves / RESOUNDworship.org
(Admin by The Jubilate Group - copyrightmanager@jubilate.co.uk)

CCLI# 7073062

COME, COME AS YOU ARE
(COME AS YOU ARE)

Key = G

Zach Neese,
Harvey Jessop & Pete James

Copyright © 2016 Gateway Create Publishing/BMI (adm. by Music Services, Inc.)
Harvey Jessop/Pete James

CCLI# 7079671

31

9

COME, LORD JESUS, IN YOUR GLORY
(COME, LORD JESUS)

Key = G

Chris Eaton,
Sam & Becki Cox

♩ = 72

1. Come, Lord Je - sus, in your glo - ry, come and fill this place.
2. Come, Lord Je - sus, my re - deem - er, breathe on me a - new;
3. Come, Lord Je - sus, King of hea - ven, come in vic - to - ry;

Come and have your way a - mong us as we seek your face.
search me, know me, Sa - viour make me more and more like you.
now the dark - ness is de - feat - ed, you have set us free.

When we lay our cares be - fore you, may our striv - ings cease.
Changed from glo - ry in - to glo - ry, till we're face to face.
It is fin - ished, death is beat - en, love has o - ver - come.
4. Join - ing with the saints and an - gels, prais - ing you a - lone;

Copyright © 2016 Freedom Sounds (Adm Song Solutions www.songsolutions.org)/
Clouseau Music/SGO Music Publishing Ltd (PRS)

CCLI# 7064923

THIS SONG IS FEATURED ON **NEWSONGS FOR THE CHURCH 2017**

As we wor-ship and a-dore you, lead us to your
Ran-somed, res-cued, healed and ho-ly by your sav-ing
ev-'ry tear will turn to glad-ness, ev-'ry bat-tle
there we'll be with you for-e-ver, our e-ter-nal

— peace.
— grace.
— home.
— won.

— grace.

10

COME THOU FOUNT OF EV'RY BLESSING
(JESUS FOUNT)

Key = C

Original Words: Robert Robinson 1758
Music: Nettleton/Additional music & Words: Phil Moore/Colin Webster

Copyright © 2016 Colin Webster Songs & Phil Moore Songs
(Adm Song Solutions www.songsolutions.org)

CCLI# 7069235

mount, I'm fixed up - on it, mount of God's un - chang - ing
heart, Lord, take and seal it, seal it for thy courts a - bove. } Je - sus,
res - cue me from dan - ger bought me with his pre - cious blood. }

fount of ev - 'ry bless - ing, tune my heart to sing your grace; for your mer - cies, ne - ver

ceas - ing, call for songs of loud - est praise.

3. Hi - ther praise. Je - sus,
Je - sus,

praise.

11

EVEN THOUGH I WALK
(YOU COVER ME)

Key = G

Paul Baloche,
Krissy Nordhoff & Michael Neale

Copyright © 2016 Integrity's Praise! Music/Michael Neale Music/Integrity Worship Music/Leadworship Songs/
Integrity's Alleluia! Music/Nordinary Music (Adm. by CapitolCMGPublishing.com excl. UK,
adm. by Integrity Music, part of the David C Cook family, songs@integritymusic.com)

CCLI# 7065491

— wings.
— song.

Chorus 𝄋 G (*Last Ch. D.S.*)

You co - ver____ me, you co - ver____ me, I'm

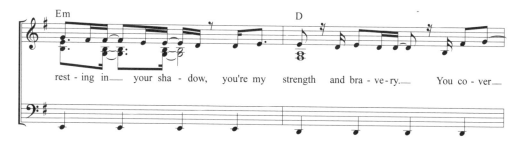

rest - ing in____ your sha - dow, you're my strength and bra - ve - ry.____ You co - ver____

— me, you co - ver____ me, I'm safe in - side__ your pre - sence, you hold back

D.S. (last chorus repeat) x 3 — 2° inst.

Last time to Coda ⊕ 1. (*to v.2*)

— the e - ne - my,__ you co - ver____ me.
(you co - ver)

37

38

THE LORD IS A REFUGE FOR THE OPPRESSED, A STRONGHOLD IN TIMES OF TROUBLE.

PSALM 9:9

FATHER OF KINDNESS
(YES AND AMEN)

Key = D

Anthony Brown,
Chris McClarney & Nate Moore

Verse

1. Fa - ther of kind - ness, you have poured out grace,— you
2. Beau - ti - ful Sa - viour, you have brought me here;— you

brought me out— of dark - ness, you have filled— me— with peace.
pulled me from— the ash - es, you have bro - ken ev - 'ry curse.—

Gi - ver of mer - cy, you're my help in time of need,— Lord,
Bles - sed Re - deem - er, you have set this cap - tive free,— Lord,

% Chorus

I can't help but sing:— Faith - ful,— you are;— faith - ful, for - e-
I can't help but sing:—

Copyright © 2016 Thankyou Music (Adm. by CapitolCMGPublishing.com excl. UK,
adm. by Integrity Music, part of the David C Cook family, songs@integritymusic.com) /
Bethel Worship Publishing/Mouth of the River Music/Tony Brown Music Designee
(Adm Song Solutions www.songsolutions.org)

CCLI# 7048885

THIS SONG IS
FEATURED ON
**NEWSONGS FOR THE
CHURCH 2017**

FROM HEAVEN TO EARTH OUR SAVIOUR CAME
(HE LIVES)

Key = D♭

Ben Cantelon, Chris Tomlin,
Nick Herbert & Reuben Morgan

Capo 1 (C)

♩ = 76

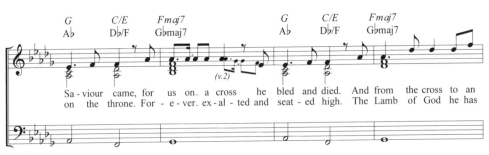

Copyright © 2016 Thankyou Music/Ben Cantelon Designee/Safe & Sound Music (Adm. by CapitolCMGPublishing.com excl. UK & Europe,
adm. by Integrity Music, part of the David C Cook family, songs@integritymusic.com) /Sixsteps Songs/S. D. G. Publishing/
Worship Together Music (Adm. by CapitolCMGPublishing.com excl. UK, adm. by Integrity Music,
part of the David C Cook family, songs@integritymusic.com) / SHOUT! Music Publishing

CCLI# 7072571

THIS SONG IS FEATURED ON
NEWSONGS FOR THE CHURCH 2017

GIVE ME ALL ETERNITY
(GOD MOST HIGH)

Key = A

Michael Farren, Corey Voss
& Tony Wood

Copyright © 2016 Integrity's Alleluia! Music/Corey Michael Voss/Farren Love & War (Adm. by CapitolCMGPublishing.com excl. UK, adm. by Integrity Music, part of the David C Cook family, songs@integritymusic.com) / Wordspring Music, LLC/Tony Wood Songs (Adm Song Solutions www.songsolutions.org)

CCLI# 7058237

GOD IN THE HERE AND NOW
(WE STAND)

Key = A

Mark Tedder & Trevor Michael

1. God in the here and now, in the com-ing and the go-
2. God of the weak and strong, be our re-fuge, our de-fend-

- ing. God in the fear and doubt, in the se-
- er. God when it's all gone wrong, be our com-

- cret and the know-ing. We're keep-ing our eyes
- fort, we sur-ren-der. We're keep-ing our eyes

Copyright © Mark Tedder Publishing & 7Core Music Publishing
(Adm Song Solutions www.songsolutions.org)

CCLI# 7078888

47

48

GOD TAKE US BACK, THE PLACE WE BEGAN
(SIMPLE PURSUIT)

Ben Cantelon, Matt Redman,
Nick Herbert & Sam Bailey

♪ = 124

1. God take us back,___ the place we be-gan,___ the sim-ple pur-suit___ of no-thing but you.___

(v.2)
The in-no - cence of
2. Keep our hearts real,

a heart in your hands,___
keep your grace___ close.

God take us back,-
You're bring-ing us back,-

Copyright © 2016 Thankyou Music/Said & Done Music/Ben Cantelon Designee (Adm. by CapitolCMGPublishing.com
excl. UK & Europe, adm. by Integrity Music, part of the David C Cook family, songs@integritymusic.com)/sixsteps Music/
worshiptogether.com Songs (Adm. by CapitolCMGPublishing.com excl. UK, adm. by Integrity Music, part of the David C Cook family,
songs@integritymusic.com)/Bespoke Records (Adm. excl UK by SHOUT!
Music Publishing) www.bespokerecords.com

49

CCLI# 7054551

oh, God, take us back___
you're bring-ing us home { to an un-swerv-ing faith___

in the pow'r of your name___ A heart beat-ing for your king-dom to reign.

A church that is known___ for your pre-sence a-gain.___ God take us

Chorus (2,3, 8va)

back. No-thing and no___ one comes close to___ you,

50

no-thing could e - ver come close.   No-thing and no— one; it's you, and you on - ly,

1.   **D.S.(v.2)** | **2.,3.,4.   D.S.S. (2° Inst)**

no-thing   could e - ver come   close.   close.

4.

close.

Photocopy this legally
with an MRL Licence
from ccli.co.uk

17

GOD THE UNCREATED ONE
(KING FOREVERMORE)

Key = G

Pete James
& Aaron Keyes

♩ = 65

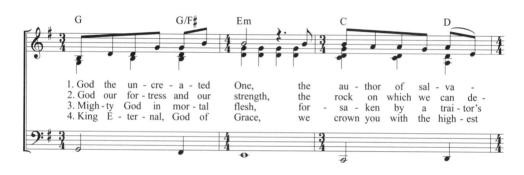

1. God the un-cre-a-ted One, the au-thor of sal-va-
2. God our for-tress and our strength, the rock on which we can de-
3. Migh-ty God in mor-tal flesh, for-sa-ken by a trai-tor's
4. King E-ter-nal, God of Grace, we crown you with the high-est

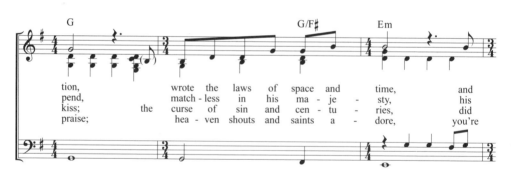

tion, wrote the laws of space and time, and
pend, match-less in his ma-je-sty, his
kiss; the curse of sin and cen-tu-ries, did
praise; hea-ven shouts and saints a-dore, you're

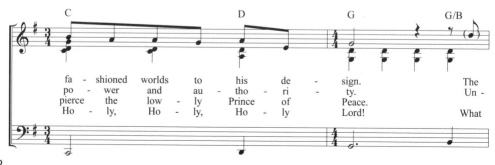

fa-shioned worlds to his de-sign. The
po-wer and au-tho-ri-ty. Un-
pierce the low-ly Prince of Peace. Ho-
Ho-ly, Ho-ly, Ho-ly Lord! What

Copyright © 2016 Thankyou Music (Adm. by CapitolCMGPublishing.com excl. UK & Europe,
adm. by Integrity Music, part of the David C Cook family, songs@integritymusic.com) / Aaron Keyes designee

CCLI# 7057478

GRANDER EARTH HAS QUAKED BEFORE
(IT IS WELL)

Key = G

Kristene DiMarco

Copyright © 2014 Bethel Music Publishing
(Adm Song Solutions www.songsolutions.org)

CCLI# 7021972

55

56

HE IS ALIVE
(THIS CHANGES EVERYTHING)

Key = G

Lou & Nathan Fellingham
and Tom Read

57

Copyright © 2016 Thankyou Music (Adm. by CapitolCMGPublishing.com excl. UK & Europe,
adm. by Integrity Music, part of the David C Cook family, songs@integritymusic.com)

CCLI# 7076299

58

HE LAVISHES GRACE AS OUR BURDENS GROW GREATER
(EVERLASTING ARMS)

Key = C

Verse words by Annie J. Flint
Adapt. & Chorus by Lou Fellingham,
Chris Eaton & Abby Eaton

♩ = 74

1. He la-vish-es grace as our bur-dens grow great-er; he sends us more strength as our la-bours in-crease. To ad-ded af-flic-tions he of-fers more mer-cy;

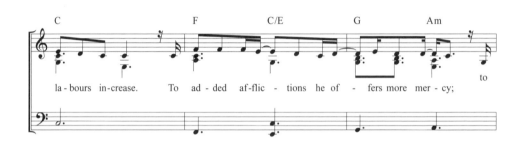

to mul-ti-plied tri-als he mul-ti-plies peace.

2. When

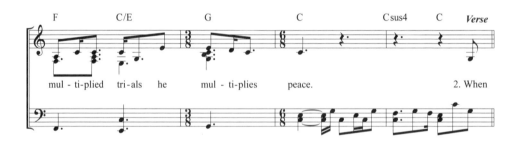

(v.3)

we have ex-haus-ted our store of en-du-rance, when our strength has failed and the
love has no li-mits, his grace has no mea-sure, his pow'r has no boun-d'ry that's

Copyright © 2016 Thankyou Music (Adm. by CapitolCMGPublishing.com excl. UK & Europe,
adm. by Integrity Music, part of the David C Cook family, songs@integritymusic.com)/
Clouseau Music (admin. by Bug Music Inc)

CCLI# 7076790

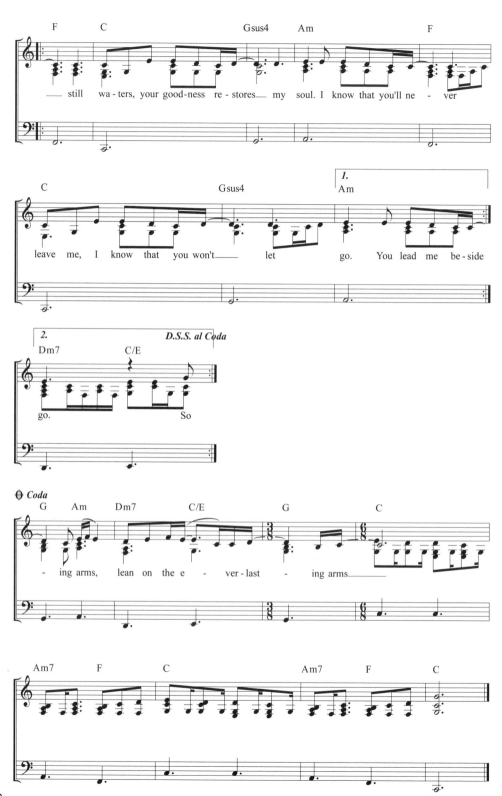

still wa-ters, your good-ness re-stores my soul. I know that you'll ne - ver

leave me, I know that you won't let go. You lead me be-side

2. *D.S.S. al Coda*

go. So

Coda

- ing arms, lean on the e - ver-last - ing arms.

HE'S COMING ON
THE CLOUDS
(LION AND THE LAMB)

Key = A♭

Capo 1 (G)

Brenton Brown, Leeland Mooring
& Brian Johnson

1. He's com-ing on the clouds, kings and king-doms will bow down.
2. O-pen up the gate, make way be-fore the King of kings.

And ev-'ry chain will break as bro-ken hearts de-clare his praise.
The God who comes to save is here to set the cap-tives free.

Who can stop the Lord Al-migh-ty?
For who can stop the Lord Al-migh-ty?

Our God is a Li-

Copyright © 2015 Thankyou Music (Adm. by CapitolCMGPublishing.com excl. UK & Europe,
adm. by Integrity Music, part of the David C Cook family, songs@integritymusic.com)
/Bethel Music/Meaux Mercy/The Devil Is A Liar! Publishing (Adm Song Solutions www.songsolutions.org)

CCLI# 7038281

64

22

HEAR OUR CRY, OH KING OF HEAVEN
(HOPE AND GLORY)

Key = D

Tim Hughes,
Martin Smith & Nick Herbert

Verse
1. Hear our cry,___ oh King of hea-ven, Je-sus hope___ to ev-'ry heart. We are lost___ with-out your glo-ry; We are lost___ with-out you God.
2. Be the fire,___ that burns with-in us, flames of love___ that pu-ri-fy. Send your pow'r___ and your sal-va-tion, let us see___ your King-dom come.
3. eyes___ and show us mer-cy; how we need___ your Fa-ther's love. Lead us home,___ and out of dark-ness, with your gos-pel, burn-ing bright. On-ly *(v.3 Jump to Chorus)*

On-ly 2. Be the On-ly

Chorus
Last time to Coda
you___ can move the moun-tain, on-ly you___ can heal our___ land; Christ a-lone, our hope and

66

Copyright © 2015 Thankyou Music/Gloworks/Tim Hughes Designee
(Adm. by CapitolCMGPublishing.com excl. UK & Europe, adm. by Integrity Music,
part of the David C Cook family, songs@integritymusic.com)

CCLI# 7043793

67

If you need help to find a song on a particular theme or Scripture passage, or just want to know which of the Spring Harvest songbooks or albums features the song you're after - use our song search.

» search online at **www.springharvest.org/songsearch**

essentialchristian.org

NEW BIBLE STUDY RESOURCE

SPRING HARVEST | BIBLE STUDIES

One for a purpose:
Unity in Christ
7 sessions for group study

GAVIN & ANNE CALVER

Unity

Specially designed for small groups and individuals, this workbook contains material for seven sessions and a prayer resource section. Sessions include a Bible passage, key thoughts and comments, questions to reflect upon or discuss, action points and prayer guidance.

Available at essentialchristian.org/store and Christian Bookshops

HOW SWEET THE NAME OF JESUS SOUNDS
(O PRAISE THE NAME)

Key = D

Words: John Newton (1725-1807)
Music & Additional Words: Phil Moore & Colin Webster

1. How sweet the Name of Je - sus sounds in a be - liev - er's ear! It soothes his sor - rows, heals his wounds and drives a - way his fear. It makes the wound - ed spi - rit whole and calms the trou - bled breast; 'tis man - na to the

2. Dear Name, the rock on which I build, my shield and hid - ing - place, my ne - ver - fail - ing trea - s'ry, filled with bound - less stores of grace! Je - sus! my Shep - herd, Bro - ther, Friend my Proph - et, Priest and King, my Lord, my Life, my

3. Weak is the ef - fort of my heart and cold my warm - est thought, but when I see you face to face I'll praise you as I ought. Till then I would your love pro - claim with ev - 'ry fleet - ing breath, and may the mu - sic

Copyright © 2015 Colin Webster Songs & Phil Moore Songs
(Adm Song Solutions www.songsolutions.org)

CCLI# 7069234

hun - gry soul and to the wea - ry, rest.
Way, my End, ac - cept the praise I bring.
of your Name re - fresh my soul in death!

O

praise the name of Je - sus, the name high o - ver all. the high - est heav'n can-

Last time to Coda ⊕ | 1.,2.   D.C. | 3.   D.S.

not con - tain its great - ness and its great - ness and its pow'r.

O

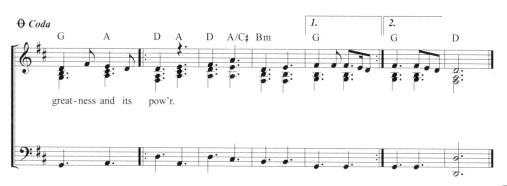

⊕ *Coda*

great - ness and its pow'r.

I CAST MY MIND TO CALVARY
(O PRAISE THE NAME (ANÁSTASIS))

Key = C

Benjamin Hastings,
Dean Ussher & Marty Sampson

Copyright © 2015 Hillsong Music Publishing
publishing@hillsong.com

CCLI # 7037787

73

I ONCE WAS LOST, I WALKED AWAY
(YOUR MERCY)

Key = E

Paul Baloche,
Andi Rozier & Jonathan Smith

1. I once was lost, I walked a-way; The road was dark, I could not see. My hope was gone, the pain was real, but your mer-cy.

2. You saw my steps, you felt my fears; you heard my cries, you caught my tears. Arms o-pen wide you ran to me with your mer-cy.

3. life be-yond the grave, my deep-est shame is cast a-way. You sing a song that co-vers me, it's your mer-cy.

2. You saw my

Chorus: Your mer-cy, your mer-cy, I stand be-fore my King and bow my heart to sing: you saved me, you raised me.

You died so I could live, no great-er love than this, your mer-cy.

4th time D.S. (last Chorus repeat)
Last time to Coda

Copyright © 2016 Integrity Worship Music/Leadworship Songs (Adm. by CapitolCMGPublishing.com excl. UK, adm. by Integrity Music,
part of the David C Cook family, songs@integritymusic.com) / Be Essential Songs/Harvest Worship Songs/
Not Just Another Song Publishing/So Essential Tunes (Admin by Essential Music Publishing LLC)

CCLI# 7060745

75

26

IN THIS WORLD WE WILL FACE TRIBULATION
(WE STAND AS ONE)

Key = D♭

Steve Merkel,
Don Poythress & Greg Sykes

Capo 1 (C)

♩ = 110

Copyright © 2016 Integrity Worship Music/Integrity's Praise! Music (Adm. by CapitolCMGPublishing.com excl. UK,
adm. by Integrity Music, part of the David C Cook family, songs@integritymusic.com)
/Clear Brooks Music (Adm Song Solutions www.songsolutions.org)

CCLI# 7054980

what can stand a-gainst us when we stand_____ as_____ one!

One Bride,_____ one bo - dy,_____

one voice, one heart - beat,_____ one name high a - bove__ all__ o - thers:

Je - sus,_____ on-ly Je - sus._____

1st time D.C. v.2
Last time to Coda ✦

Bridge

D.S. al Coda

✦ *Coda*

27

I'VE HEARD A THOUSAND STORIES OF WHAT THEY THINK YOU'RE LIKE
(GOOD GOOD FATHER)

Key = A

Pat Barrett & Tony Brown

Copyright © 2014 sixsteps Music/Vamos Publishing/worshiptogether.com songs (Adm. by CapitolCMGPublishing.com excl. UK,
adm. by Integrity Music, part of the David C Cook family, songs@integritymusic.com) / Capitol CMG Paragon/
Common Hymnal Publishing/Housefires Sounds/Tony Brown Publishing Designee
(Adm Song Solutions www.songsolutions.org)

CCLI# 7036612

80

D.S.(with repeat) al Coda

✛ *Coda*

Photocopy this legally
with an MRL Licence
from ccli.co.uk

JESUS, NAME I CAN'T FORGET
(OUR GOD (NO PLACE WITHOUT HOPE))

Key = C

Sam Archer
& Simon Parkin

♩ = 110

Verse

1. Je - sus, name I can't for - get, the
your voice has called me home, with

find - er and the keep - er of my soul. Je-sus, if I
pro - mi-ses of mer - cy and new life. Je-sus, like a

(v.2 8va)

wan - der in the night, you will search for me be-yond the morn - ing light.
fa - ther and his child, you em - brace me when I stag - ger from the wild.

Pre-Chorus

There's no place I could run to hide from you. There's no place I could run

to hide from you.

Copyright © 2016 Sam Archer/
Admin by ARKYARD

CCLI# 7071363

THIS SONG IS
FEATURED ON
**NEWSONGS FOR THE
CHURCH 2017**

Chorus

Our God is al-ways faith-ful, our God is al-ways by our side.

1.

2.,3.,4. (Last time 8vb)

2. Je-sus, Our God is ne-ver fail-ing, our God for-e-ver glo-ri-

D.S. al Fine

(Fine)

fied.

Bridge

There is no place with-out hope, there is

no place with-out hope. You've got the whole world in your hands, you've got the whole

1.

2.

D.S.

world in your hands. There is world in your hands.

29 LET THE KING OF MY HEART
(KING OF MY HEART)

Key = A

John Mark McMillan
& Sarah McMillan

Copyright © 2015 Meaux Jeaux Music / Raucous Ruckus Publishing
(Adm CapitolCMGpublishing.com UK&Eire Song Solutions www.songsolutions.org)
& Sarah McMillan Publishing Designee

CCLI# 7046145

30

LISTEN TO THE WORDS OF
THE RISEN CHRIST
(PEACE BE WITH YOU)

Key = C

Joel Payne

Lis-ten to the words of the ri-sen Christ: peace be with you.

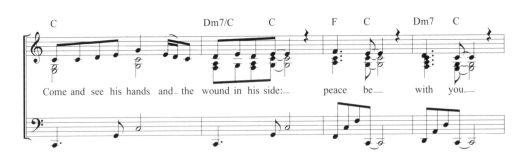

Come and see his hands and the wound in his side: peace be with you.

With the eyes of faith are you rea-dy to see? peace be with you.

Come with all your doubts for it's time to be-lieve: peace be with you,

Words & music: © Joel Payne / RESOUNDworship.org
(Admin by The Jubilate Group - copyrightmanager@jubilate.co.uk)

CCLI# 7066092

87

31

MY HOPE IS BUILT ON
NOTHING LESS
(CORNERSTONE)

Key = C

♩ = 72

Jonas Myrin, Reuben Morgan & Eric Liljero
Verses from 'The Solid Rock' by Edward Mote (Trad.)

1. My hope is built on nothing less than Jesus' blood and righteousness; I dare not trust the sweetest frame but wholly trust in Jesus' name.
2. When darkness seems to hide his face I rest on his unchanging grace; in ev'ry high and stormy gale my anchor holds within the veil, my anchor holds within the veil.
3. When he shall come with trumpet sound, oh may I then in him be found; dressed in his righteousness alone, faultless stand before the throne.

Christ a-

Copyright © 2011 Hillsong Music Publishing
publishing@hillsong.com

CCLI# 6158927

32

MY LIFE IS A STORY BOUGHT BY GRACE
(DEVOTION)

Key = C

Luke Hellebronth,
Dean Ussher & Tim Hughes

1. My life is a sto - ry bought by grace;___ love un - re - lent -
2. Your rich - es of mer - cy o - ver - flow;___ love that sur - pas -

- ing, called my name.___ Oh what a my - st'ry,___ oh___ what grace,
- ses all___ I know,___ I'm filled with the won - der of who___ you___ are,

_ I___ am___ changed.___ All my af - fec - tion,___ all of my praise,
_ who___ you___ are.

all my de - vo - tion, for all of my days.___ Pour out my wor - ship,___ lift up your name.

_ Je - sus you're all___ that__ I need - ed___ and more.

Copyright © 2016 Thankyou Music (Adm. by CapitolCMGPublishing.com
excl. UK & Europe, adm. by Integrity Music, part of the David C Cook family,
songs@integritymusic.com)/SHOUT! Music Publishing

CCLI# 7078246

33

O VICTORY, YOU HAVE WON
(CHAMPION)

Key = G

Bryan Torwalt & Katie Torwalt

♩ = 84

Verse lyrics:

1. O vic-to-ry, you have won; vic-to-ri-ous, you have come.
   What was sto-len, you brought back to us.

2. The One in whom we be-long, we'll lift our voice, join his song.
   We were or-phaned, now for-e-ver yours.

Chorus:
Our Cham-pi-on, you fight for us, you made a way where there was none. Our Cham-pi-on, you're strong in us, the debt we owed, you paid in blood.

1st time D.C.(v.2)
3rd time D.S. al Coda
Last time to Coda

Copyright © 2016 Capitol CMG Paragon/Capitol CMG Genesis/Jesus Culture Music Group/Jesus
Culture Music (Adm Capitolcmgpublishing.com/UK&Eire Song Solutions www.songsolutions.org)

CCLI# 7065984

THIS SONG IS FEATURED ON **NEWSONGS FOR THE CHURCH 2017**

34

OH THE THOUGHT, THE WRATH THAT I HAD EARNED
(HOW GREAT THE LOVE OF JESUS)

Key = C

Nathan Fellingham & Michael Farren

1. Oh the thought, the wrath that I had earned, swal-lowed up, in
way, this bit-ter re-me-dy, took my shame, and

an-guish un-de-served. On a cross, where mer-cy stood dis-played,
gave new life to me. Once the vil-est sin-ner now be-loved,

spill-ing blood, that ran to make a way. Oh your love so
firm-ly held, by all your grace has done.

cap-ti-vat-ing, wraps me up I can't e-scape it.

Copyright © 2016 Thankyou Music (Adm. by CapitolCMGPublishing.com excl. UK & Europe, adm. by Integrity Music,
part of the David C Cook family, songs@integritymusic.com)/Integrity's Alleluia! Music/Farren Love and War Publishing
(Adm. by CapitolCMGPublishing.com excl. UK, adm. by Integrity Music,
part of the David C Cook family, songs@integritymusic.com)

CCLI# 7064609

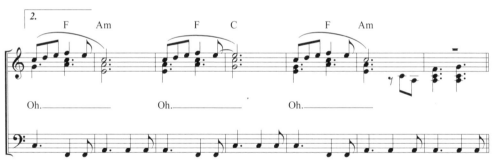

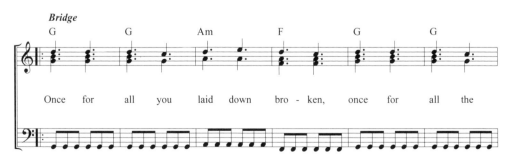

95

of – fer – ing, once for all you robbed the grave, to

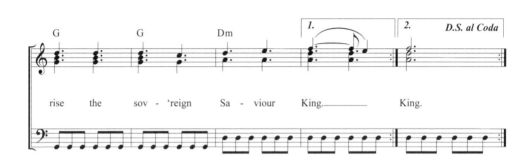

rise the sov - 'reign Sa - viour King._____ King.

Je - sus, how__ great the__ love of Je - sus.

96

OH WE LOOK TO THE SON
(LOOK TO THE SON)

Key = C

Joel Houston, Marty Sampson, Matt Crocker,
Reuben Morgan & Scott Ligertwood

Copyright © 2016 Hillsong Music Publishing
publishing@hillsong.com

CCLI# 7068422

See the king - dom burst into co - lour at the speed of light.
See the hope of hea - ven shin - ing like the ris - ing sun.

Free - dom shak - ing up the at - mo - sphere,
Now for-e - ver lift - ed up from death to life,

as the sha - dows fade into no -
there's no fear in love, and no dark -

- thing, as the day ap - pears.
- ness in his end - less light.

Pre-Chorus

Be-yond the

skies a - bove, love reach-ing out for us. The e-ver-

98

ON THE CROSS YOU WERE BROKEN
(SING IT OUT (HE'S ALIVE))

Key = F

Tom Eccleshall, Sarah Eccleshall,
Stephen William & Gabriel Wilson

Copyright © 2016 KXC Publishing
(Adm SHOUT! Music Publishing/HMTR Limited)

CCLI# 7055444

ONCE BOUND BY FEAR, SO LOST IN SIN
(OUR STORY OUR SONG)

Key = B♭

Dustin Smith,
Krissy Nordhoff & Jonathan Walker

Capo 3 (G)

Copyright © 2016 Integrity's Alleluia! Music/Integrity's Praise! Music/Nordinary Music/Prestonwood Creative Publishing
(Adm. by CapitolCMGPublishing.com excl. UK, adm. by Integrity Music,
part of the David C Cook family, songs@integritymusic.com)

CCLI# 7065454

Chorus

This, this is our sto - ry,— this, this is our song:— we are prais - ing, prais-ing our Sa - viour— all the day_ long,— all the day_ long.—

1st time D.C.(v.2)
3rd time D.S. al Coda

Last time to Coda

Oh,— oh,— oh,— oh.—

Bridge

No-thing's gon-na keep our voi-ces si-lent; no-thing's gon-na bind us, we are free. No-

D.S.

- thing's gon-na shake these hearts u-ni-ted; no-thing's gon-na stop our te-sti-mo-ny.

Coda

Oh.

38

ONE CHURCH, ONE FAITH, ONE ANTHEM RAISED
(GOD AND GOD ALONE)

Key = B

Jonas Myrin,
Jason Ingram & Chris Tomlin

Capo 4 (G)

♩ = 76

Verse

1. One church, one faith, one an-them raised; God and God a-lone.
One cross, one grace, one name that saves, all praise to you be-longs, all praise to you be-longs.

else can wash our sin a-way?— God and God a-lone.
Who else can raise us from the— grave? All praise to you be-longs, all praise to you be-longs.

Chorus

We lift you high-er,— high-er,— God and God a-lone; your name be-longs.

Copyright © 2016 sixsteps Songs/S.D.G Publishing/Worship Together Music (Adm. by CapitolCMGPublishing.com excl. UK, adm. by Integrity Music,
part of the David C Cook family, songs@integritymusic.com)/ Open Hands Music/So Essential Tunes (Admin by Essential Music Publishing LLC)/
Son of the Lion (Admin by SHOUT! Music Publishing UK)/Capitol CMG Paragon
(Adm Song Solutions www.songsolutions.org)

CCLI# 7054550

loud - er,_ loud - er_ than a - ny o - ther song. You are for - e - ver seat - ed on your_

_throne, you are for - e - ver God and God a - lone.
(We lift you)   2. Who

lone. You are for - e - ver God and God a - lone.   And

lone. What could se - pa - rate us from this a - maz - ing love?

What could say it's great - er than our God? Ev - 'ry knee will bow down._

105

Oh, Oh, ev-'ry knee will bow down.

We lift you Yes, ev-'ry knee will bow down.

Oh, ev-'ry knee will bow down.

THIS SONG IS FEATURED ON **NEWSONGS FOR THE CHURCH 2017**

essential christian

essentialchristian.org

Your Online Christian Resource Store

With over 180,000 resources, including:

- Books
- Music
- Bibles
- Song Scores
- Teaching
- DVDs
- Church Supplies
- Cards and Gifts

essentialchristian.org/store

39

PRAISE BE TO OUR GOD
(O WHAT LOVE THAT CAME)

Key = A

Cathy Burton & Nathan Jess

1. Praise be to our God, praise his ho - ly name.___ He
(2.) Je - sus I will trust, my hope in him is sure,___ He

chose to walk with us,___ take on the hu - man frame.___ And O___
seeks and saves the lost,___ and o - pens hea - ven's___ door. And O

what love___ that came,___ to save___ my wan - d'ring soul;___ and O___

the price___ he paid,___ for me___ to be___ made whole.___ 2. In

Copyright © 2016 Song Solutions www.songsolutions.org/Thankyou Music (Adm. by CapitolCMGPublishing.com
excl. UK, adm. by Integrity Music, part of the David C Cook family, songs@integritymusic.com)

CCLI# 7072048

SPRING HARVEST

NEWSONGS FOR THE CHURCH 2017

THIS SONG IS FEATURED ON **NEWSONGS FOR THE CHURCH 2017**

Res - cu - er,___ poured out his___ love;___ Li - be - ra -

- tor,___ bro - ken for___ us.___ Res - cu - er,___ rose from

___ the grave, Li - be - ra - tor,___ with the po - wer to save.___

D.S. al Coda

And O___

Coda

___ Praise be to our God, praise his ho - ly name.___

40

SPIRIT OF GOD, COME CLEANSE, RENEW
(EVERY NATION UNDER HEAVEN)

Key = C

Tom McConnell

Copyright © 2016 Song Solutions Daybreak
www.songsolutions.org

CCLI# 7063395

111

so we're giv - ing our lives, and we're trust - ing your grace.

1.

2.,3. *Bridge*

2. As we turn from sin

We are giv-ing our lives and we're trust-ing your

Last time to Coda

grace.

D.S. al Coda

Coda

112

THE GRACE OF GOD HAS REACHED FOR ME
(THE LORD IS MY SALVATION)

Key = A

Jonas Myrin, Keith Getty,
Kristyn Getty & Nathan Nockels

Copyright © 2016 Getty Music Publishing/Sweater Weather Music
(Adm CapitolCMGpublishing.com UK&EIRE Song Solutions www.songsolutions.org)
& Son Of The Lion/HMTR Limited

CCLI# 7063694

Lord is our sal - va - tion.___ The Lord is our sal - va - tion.___

SPRING HARVEST
song search

If you need help to find a song on a particular theme or Scripture passage, or just want to know which of the Spring Harvest songbooks or albums features the song you're after - use our song search.

» search online at **www.springharvest.org/songsearch**

42

THERE IS A GOD WHO HAS WALKED UPON HIS EARTH
(EMMANUEL)

Key = D

Sam Cox, Becki Cox
& Mark Tedder

♩ = 123 **Verse**

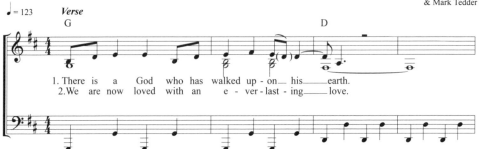

1. There is a God who has walked up-on his earth.
2. We are now loved with an e-ver-last-ing love.

There is a king who would leave his throne and serve.
We are now free by his work up-on the cross.

There is a friend with a love that calms our fear.
We are not bound by a past that holds us down.

There is a Sa-viour, there is a heal-er here. With Je-
We are for-gi-ven, we have a fu-ture now!

Copyright © 2016 Freedom Sounds/Mark Tedder Publishing
(Adm Song Solutions www.songsolutions.org)

CCLI# 7064924

117

THERE IS A HILL I CHERISH
(CROWNS)

Key = G

Benjamin Hastings,
Michael Fatkin & Scott Groom

Copyright © 2016 Hillsong Music Publishing
publishing@hillsong.com

CCLI# 7068421

THERE'S NOTHING WORTH MORE
(HOLY SPIRIT, YOU ARE WELCOME HERE)

Key = A

Bryan Torwalt & Katie Torwalt

1. There's no-thing worth more,____ that will e-ver come close,____
2. I've tast-ed and seen,____ of the sweet-est of loves,____

____ no-thing can com-pare,____ you're____ our liv-ing hope
____ where my heart be-comes free,____ and my shame is un -

____ your____ pre-sence.
- done____ in your pre-sence, Lord.

Chorus

Ho-ly Spi-rit, you are wel-come here, come

Copyright © 2011 Jesus Culture Music/Capitol CMG Genesis
(Adm Capitolcmgpublishing.com/UK&Eire Song Solutions www.songsolutions.org)

CCLI# 6087919

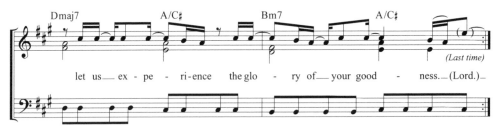

let us— ex - pe - ri-ence the glo - ry of— your good - ness.— (Lord.)—

(Last time)

D.S. al Coda

𝄋 *Coda*

pre - sence, Lord.——

Photocopy this legally
with an MRL Licence
from ccli.co.uk

essentialchristian.org

Copyright and Publishing for Christian Songwriters

Song Solutions is a music publisher and administrator specialising in Christian and Gospel music with over 25 years of experience in handling every aspect of copyright administration worldwide.

WRITERS

Have you written a song for the Church? Find out how we can help.

PUBLISHERS

We can get your songs and catalogues heard worldwide.

LICENSING

Require a license, or not sure which one you need? Get in touch!

Find out more at songsolutions.org or call 01825 748893

THOUGH THE TEARS MAY FALL MY SONG WILL RISE
(JOY OF THE LORD)

Key = D

Rend Collective
& Ed Cash

1. Though the tears may fall my song will rise, my song will rise to you. Though my
   dead of night, I'll lift my eyes, I'll lift my eyes to you. When the
   can - not see you with my eyes, let faith a - rise to you. When I
   shine with glo - ry, Lord of light, I feel a - live with you. In your

heart may fail my song will rise, my song will rise to You. While there's
wa - ters rise I'll lift my eyes, I'll lift my eyes to you. While there's
can - not feel your hand in mine, let faith a - rise to you. God of
pre - sence now I come a - live I am a - live with you. There is

breath in my lungs, I will praise you Lord.
hope in this heart, I will praise you Lord.
mer - cy and love, I will praise you Lord.
strength when I say "I will praise you Lord!"

2. In the
4. Oh, you

Chorus

The joy of the Lord is my strength. The joy of the Lord is my

Copyright © 2015 Thankyou Music (Adm. by CapitolCMGPublishing.com)
excl. UK & Europe, adm. by Integrity Music, part of the David C Cook family, songs@integritymusic.com)/
Alletrop Music (Adm Song Solutions www.songsolutions.org)

CCLI# 7047091

WE ARE A FLAME THAT IS BURNING BRIGHT
(ONE FAMILY)

Key = G

Pete James & Harvey Jessop

1. We are a flame that is burn-ing bright, lift-ing hope in the dark-est times. From ev-'ry land, ev-'ry tribe and tongue, a world of hearts that are joined as one.

2. We are a-live in the king-dom come, a voice of change for the un-heard ones. A-wa-ken joy to de-feat de-spair, the grace of God is the hope we share.

Pre-Chorus
With arms o-pen wide, we are fa-mi-ly.

Chorus
So ring the bells, fling wide the doors, young and old and rich and poor:

Copyright © 2016 Song Solutions
www.songsolutions.org

CCLI# 7064700

all— a-round the— world,— one fa-mi-ly. From our neigh-bour to the far-thest land,

we car-ry light and the truth in— hand, all— a-round the world,— one fa-mi-ly.

Last time to Coda ⊕
One fa-mi-ly.———

1.

D.C. 2.

Bridge

God is love and love is end-less. God is love and

love's re-lent-less. God is love and love wins o - ver all.——

God is love and love's an o - cean. God is love and love has spo - ken.

D.S. al Coda

God is love and love wins o - ver all._____

Coda G

One fa - mi - ly. One fa - mi - ly.__ Yeah.

THIS SONG IS FEATURED ON **NEWSONGS FOR THE CHURCH 2017**

LIVE WORSHIP FROM SPRING HARVEST 2017

The live worship album captures the devotion and adoration of worship from Spring Harvest 2017. Featuring Lead Worshippers **Cathy Burton, Lou Fellingham, Pete James** and **Worship Central.**

Available at essentialchristian.org/store, iTunes and Christian Bookshops

WE BELIEVE IN ONE TRUE GOD
(APOSTLE'S CREED)

Key = D

Keith Getty, Kristyn Getty
& Stuart Townend

Copyright © 2016 Thankyou Music (Adm. by CapitolCMGPublishing.com excl. UK & Europe,
adm. by Integrity Music, part of the David C Cook family, songs@integritymusic.com)/
Getty Music (Admin. By Music Services)/Townend Songs (Adm Song Solutions www.songsolutions.org)

CCLI# 7063563

sky. And we be-lieve_ in_ Je - sus, the on-ly_ Son of_ God, born
night. The third day rose_ vic - to - rious, a - scen-ded in - to_ heav'n. Will
sin; Our bo-dies re - sur - rec - ted to e - ver - last - ing_ life. To

of the vir - gin Ma - ry who lived as one_ of us.
one day come to judge us, the liv - ing and_ the dead.
wor - ship, love and won - der be - fore the throne of Christ.

Chorus

We be-lieve in_ one true God: Fa - ther, Spi - rit, Son; one Church, one faith, one_

1.
Lord of all, His king-dom_ come.

2. *Tag* **Double speed ♩. = 124**
come.

WE FIX OUR EYES ON YOU, OUR LORD
(BE FORMED IN US)

Key = B♭

Becky Frith

Capo 3 (G)

♩ = 70

Verse

1. We fix our eyes on you, our Lord, our source of life, our Cor - ner -
minds, en - large our souls, re - vive our hearts and make us
sounds from age to age, new streams of life from an - cient

stone. Search us oh God and make us new, help us to hope and live in
whole. May we know love, may we know grace, and true com - mu - nion of the
wells. Help us to see with eyes of faith how you are mov - ing in our

1.

you. 2. Re-new our saints.
day.

%‍ Chorus

Be formed in us, be formed in

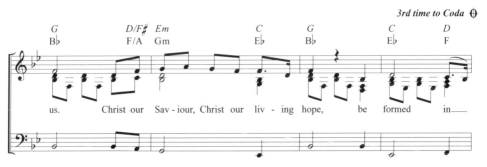

3rd time to Coda ⊕

us. Christ our Sav - iour, Christ our liv - ing hope, be formed in

Copyright © 2016 Song Solutions Daybreak
www.songsolutions.org

CCLI# 7078886

133

WE HAVE COME TO MEET WITH YOU, O GOD
(THE MOUNTAIN)

Key = A

Ben Cantelon, Nick Herbert,
Kristian Stanfill & Tim Hughes

1. We have come to meet with you, O God, we can hear you call-
2. All we need is found in you a-lone, you're the King of glo-

- ing. In this place, will you draw near to us? Ev-'ry heart is call-
- ry. Shin-ing bright for all the world to see, Je-sus, King of glo-

Chorus

- ing. 1. Lead us up the moun - tain, lead us up the moun-
- ry. - vens, o - pen up the hea-

- tain, high, in-to your pre - sence, where your glo-ry shines.
- vens, as we lift you high - er, let your glo-ry shine.

Copyright © 2016 Thankyou Music/Ben Cantelon Designee/Tim Hughes Designee (Adm. by CapitolCMGPublishing.com excl. UK & Europe,
adm. by Integrity Music, part of the David C Cook family, songs@integritymusic.com)/
worshiptogether.com Songs/sixsteps Music (Adm. by CapitolCMGPublishing.com excl. UK,
adm. by Integrity Music, part of the David C Cook family, songs@integritymusic.com)

CCLI# 7071936

1. Lead us up the moun -
2. O - pen up the hea -

Your glo - ry

(shines.)

With hearts a-ban-doned we will bold-ly ap-proach your— throne, to stand with you in glo-ry,

WHY IS UNITY IMPORTANT?

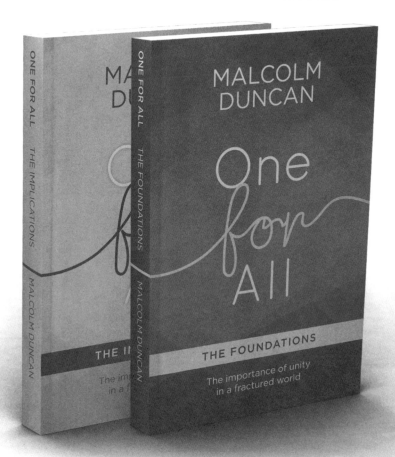

**One For All explores Christian unity in two parts:
The Foundations and The Implications.**

What did Jesus mean when he prayed for us to 'be one for one purpose', and how do we practice that today? This series* answers some tough questions, and shows us how there is far more uniting us than dividing us.

*Part 2 published July 2017

Available at essential

50

WE HAVE HOPE FOR THE COMING DAYS
(WE BELIEVE IN GOD)

Key = E

Judy Bailey

1. We have hope for the com-ing days, Ho - ly Light and it will not fail. We have hope,___ we have hope.
2. We have faith in the face of fear, built on Christ and we're ground - ed there. We have faith,___ we have faith.
3. We have love and it co - vers all, strong and sure when our peace is gone. We have love,___ we have love.
4. We have God, so we're not a - lone, by his grace, we will car - ry on. We have God,___ we have God.

Chorus

We be-lieve in God, we be-lieve God is stream-ing down through time, here with us to - day. Now what-e-ver comes, we be-lieve that God re-mains:___ Fa-ther, Son___ and Spi-rit, we be-lieve.

Last time to Coda

Copyright © 2016 Dyba Music
(Adm Song Solutions www.songsolutions.org)

CCLI# 7079571

SPRING HARVEST
NEWSONGS for THE CHURCH 2017

THIS SONG IS FEATURED ON **NEWSONGS FOR THE CHURCH 2017**

51

WE SEEK YOUR KINGDOM

Key = C

Music: Abide With Me (Henry Francis Lyte)
Lyrics: Andy Flannagan, Noel Robinson & Graham Hunter

1. We seek your king - dom through - out ev - ry_____ sphere, we long for hea - ven's de - mon - stra - tion
2. Be - fore all things, in him all things were_____ made, in - spir - ing cul - ture, me - di - a and
3. Peace, truth and jus - tice reign - ing ev - 'ry - where, with us be pre - sent in our pub - lic
4. For - give us Lord, when we have not en - gaged, fail - ing to scribe_____ your heart on hi - st'ry's
5. Faith - ful to go - vern e - ver may we_____ be, self - less in ser - vice, lov - ing con - stant -

here. Je - sus, your light shine bright for all to_____ see:
trade. May all our work serve your e - co - no - my:
square. Fill all who lead with your in - te - gri - ty:
page. Make us a - gain what we were made to_____ be:
ly. In ev - 'ry - thing may your au - tho - ri - ty:

trans - form, re -

5th time D.S.

vive and heal so - ci - e - ty.

Copyright © Downwardly Mobile Music/
Nu Image Music/Publisher Unknown

CCLI# 7078243

MY HEART SAYS OF YOU,
"SEEK HIS FACE!"
YOUR FACE, LORD, I WILL SEEK.

PSALM 27:8

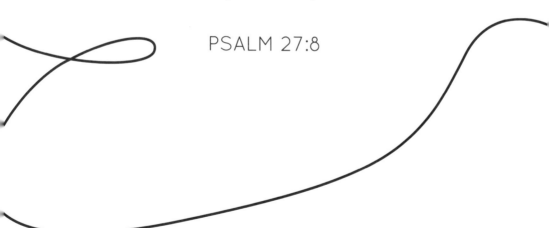

52

YOU ARE MATCHLESS IN GRACE AND MERCY
(GOD WITH US)

Key = B

Bryan Torwalt
& Katie Torwalt

Capo 4 (G)

♩ = 72

Copyright © 2015 Capitol CMG Paragon/Capitol CMG Genesis/Jesus Culture Music Group/
Jesus Culture Music (Adm Capitolcmgpublishing.com/UK&Eire Song Solutions www.songsolutions.org)

CCLI# 7054539

143

3. Your

Where there was death, you brought life, Lord. Where there was

fear, you brought cour-age. When I was a-fraid, you were with me,

and you're lift - ing me— up,   and you're lift - ing me— up.——

When there was   and you're lift - ing me— up,

and you're lift - ing me— up.———   and you're lift - ing me— up,

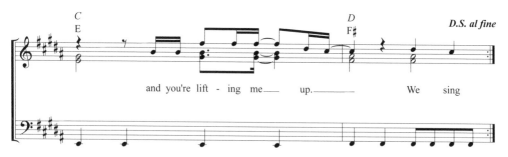

and you're lift - ing me— up.———   We   sing

53

YOU GIVE LIFE
(GREAT ARE YOU LORD)

Key = A

David Leonard,
Jason Ingram & Leslie Jordan

Copyright © 2012 Integrity's Praise! Music/Integrity's Alleluia! Music (Adm. by CapitolCMGPublishing.com
excl. the UK which is admin by Integrity Music, part of the David C Cook family,
songs@integritymusic.com) /Open Hands Music/So Essential Tuness

CCLI# 6460220

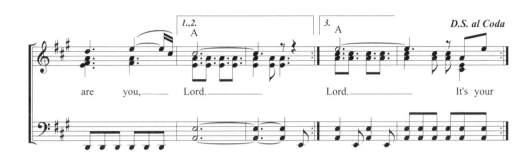

are you,____ Lord._____ Lord._____ It's your

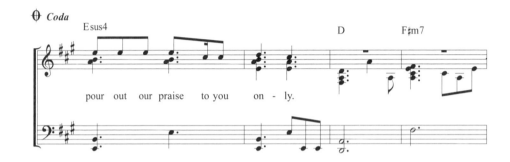

pour out our praise to you on - ly.

Photocopy this legally
with an MRL Licence
from ccli.co.uk

New Resource for School Assemblies

Deliver engaging, faith-based assemblies packed full of videos, illustrations, live drama and compelling storytelling. Developed by Spring Harvest, Big Start Assemblies streamlines the planning process by providing out-of-the-box scripts, PowerPoints, videos and music.

Meets Ofsted and SIAMS requirements for Key Stage 1 and 2

Adaptable - scripts and presentations are fully editable so you can make the content your own

Values based - Themes are built on Christian values including courage, honesty and friendship

Interactive - Engaging activities involve pupils and increase comprehension and learning

Out of the box - Everything you need to run a brilliant assembly, ready to go

Find out more and sign up for your free trial at
bigstartassemblies.org

54

YOU HAVE CALLED US OUT OF DARKEST NIGHT
(MAY THE PEOPLES PRAISE YOU)

Key = C

David Zimmer, Ed Cash, Keith Getty,
Kristyn Getty & Stuart Townend

Copyright © 2016 Townend Songs/Getty Music Publishing/Alletrop Music
(Adm Music Services/Song Solutions www.songsolutions.org)

CCLI# 7063739

151

55

YOU HEAL THE BROKEN HEARTED
(IMPOSSIBLE THINGS)

Key = D

Brenton Brown, Chris McClarney,
Chris Tomlin & Ed Cash

♩ = 110

Verse
1. You heal the bro - ken heart - ed, You set the cap - tive free,
2. Though I walk through the val - ley, dark - ness sur - round - ing me,

You lift the hea - vy bur - den, and e - ven now__ you are
there you pre - pare a__ ta - ble in the pre - sence of my

%. Chorus

lift - ing me. There is no heal - er like the Lord, our Mak - er; there is no e - qual to the
e - ne - mies

King of_ kings. Oh,__ our God is with us, we will fear no e - vil, 'cause you do im-

Copyright © 2016 Thankyou Music (Adm. by CapitolCMGPublishing.com excl. UK & Europe, adm. by Integrity Music, part of the David C Cook family,
songs@integritymusic.com)/ Sixsteps Songs/S.D.G Publishing/Worship Together Music
(Adm. by CapitolCMGPublishing.com excl. UK, adm. by Integrity Music, part of the David C Cook family,
songs@integritymusic.com) /Alletrop Music (Adm Song Solutions www.songsolutions.org)

CCLI# 7051478

56

YOU UNRAVEL ME, WITH A MELODY
(NO LONGER SLAVES)

Key = B♭

Capo 3 (G)

♩ = 74

Brian Johnson,
Jonathan David Helser & Joel Case

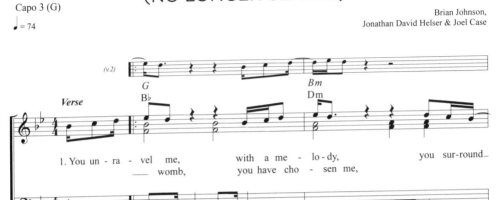

(v.2)

Verse

G
B♭

Bm
Dm

1. You un-ra-vel me, with a me-lo-dy, you sur-round
___ womb, you have cho-sen me,

C
E♭

D
F

G
B♭

___ me with___ a song___ of de-li-ve-rance from my e-ne-
love has called___ my name___ I've been born___ a-gain, in-to your fa-

Bm
Dm

C
E♭

D
F

G
B♭

Chorus

- mies till all___ my fears___ are gone.___ I'm no long-
- mi-ly, your blood___ flows through my veins.

Copyright © 2014 Bethel Music Publishing
(Adm Song Solutions www.songsolutions.org)

CCLI# 7030123

155

You split the sea, so I could walk right through it;
all my fears were drowned in per-fect love.
You res-cued me, and I_____ will stand_____ and_____ sing: I am_____
a child_____ of God._____ I'm no long-

156

YOU WERE THE WORD AT THE BEGINNING

(WHAT A BEAUTIFUL NAME)

Ben Fielding & Brooke Ligertwood

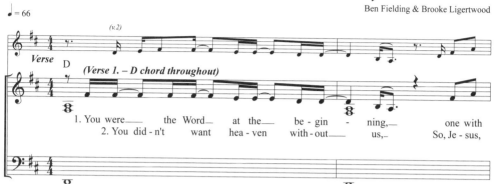

Verse

(Verse 1. – D chord throughout)

1. You were___ the Word___ at the___ be - gin - ning,___ one with
2. You did - n't want hea - ven with - out___ us,___ So, Je - sus,

God the Lord Most High;___ your hid - den glo - ry in___ cre - a -
you brought hea - ven down.___ My sin was great, your love was great -

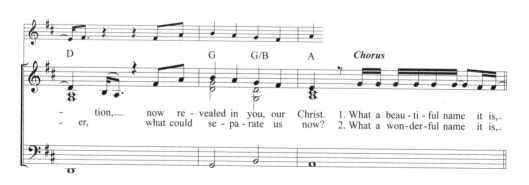

- tion,___ now re - vealed in you, our Christ. 1. What a beau - ti - ful name it is,___
- er, what could se - pa - rate us now? 2. What a won - der - ful name it is,___

Chorus

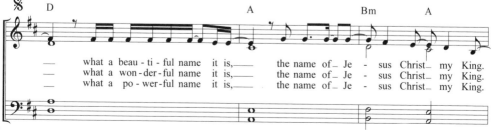

___ what a beau - ti - ful name it is,___ the name of Je - sus Christ___ my King.
___ what a won - der - ful name it is,___ the name of Je - sus Christ___ my King.
___ what a po - wer - ful name it is,___ the name of Je - sus Christ___ my King.

Copyright © 2016 Hillsong Music Publishing
publishing@hillsong.com

CCLI# 7068424

THIS SONG IS
FEATURED ON
**NEWSONGS FOR THE
CHURCH 2017**

YOU WHO FEAR THE LORD

Key = D

Jo Doré, Judy Gresham,
Carey Luce & Geraldine Luce

Verse

You who fear the Lord, do not be a-fraid;
You who wait for God, do not be dis-mayed;
You who long for rest in the day of test;
You who sit a-lone in the dark of night;

God will com-fort you and lift you up.
God who hears your pray'rs will an-swer you.
you will be re-stored to live a-gain.
look to-ward the dawn: our God will come.

Chorus

The Sun will rise, will rise, with heal-ing in his wings. (The)

(D.S. last Chorus repeat)

Words & music: © Jo Doré, Judy Gresham, Carey Luce, Geraldine Luce / RESOUNDworship.org
(Admin by The Jubilate Group - copyrightmanager@jubilate.co.uk)

CCLI# 7067770

essentialchristian.org

RECORDED TEACHING FROM SPRING HARVEST

Available on cd, dvd* and usb stick

*DVD of main meetings only

Take home and listen to talks and seminars from Spring Harvest 2017. You can choose from topics including worship leading, apologetics, parenting, mission, evangelism, discipleship, unity, encountering the Holy Spirit and more.

Over 46,000 recc   an.org/store

YOUR LOVE HAS LED ME TO SURRENDER
(SURRENDERED)

Key = B

Chris Quilala,
Brooke Ligertwood & Scott Ligertwood

162

Copyright © 2016 Capitol CMG Genesis/Jesus Culture Music
(Adm Capitolcmgpublishing.com/UK&Eire Song Solutions www.songsolutions.org)

CCLI# 7073503

YOUR LOVE SO GREAT, JESUS IN ALL THINGS
(LOVE SO GREAT)

Key = C

Joshua Grimmett,
Reuben Morgan & Jamie Snell

1. Your love so great, Jesus in all things,
2. Cre-a-tion calls all to the Sa-viour,

I've seen a glimpse of your heart. A bil-lion years, still I'll be sing-
we are a-live for your praise. In earth and sky, no one is high-

-ing. How can I praise you e-nough?
-er. Our God of won-ders, you reign.

How can I praise you e-nough?
Our God of won-ders, you reign.

You are the Lord Al-migh-ty,

out-shin-ing all the stars in glo-ry. Your love is like the wild-est o-cean,

Copyright © 2016 Hillsong Music Publishing
publishing@hillsong.com

CCLI# 7068428

BRIDGES TO C

BRIDGES TO D

BRIDGES TO E

BRIDGES TO F

BRIDGES TO G

GUITAR CHORDS

A good chord vocabulary is essential for a guitarist to feel confident when playing in worship, especially when the situation may involve reading a previously unseen piece of music or picking up a song quickly by ear. The chords on these pages are arranged in 'families' according to key.

This is a beneficial way of remembering chords as most songs stick to these groupings. For each key, the first row shows the simplest form of each chord and the second line gives a more interesting substitution. The third line shows the chords most commonly used by guitarists derived by keeping some sort of pedal tone ringing in each chord and the fourth line shows inverted chords with an alternate bass note.

Also included are the Roman Numerals and Nashville Numbers associated with each chord. If you've not come across these before, they are simply an easy way of numbering each chord within a key. This is useful as it means you can take any chord progression in one key and instantly transpose it to another. Furthermore you can try out any of the chords in each column that corresponds to the relevant Roman Numeral and see if there is chord type or inversion which still fits but adds a different flavour. Experimentation like this may open up creative chord progressions that serve as a catalyst to help you to worship in fresh ways or to write new songs.

	Roman	I	II	III	IV	V	VI	VII
	Nashville	1	2	3	4	5	6	7
Key of C	3-note chord (triad)	C	Dm	Em	F	G	Am	Bdim
	4-note chord	C maj7	D m7	E m7	F maj7	G7	A m7	B m7♭5
	Alternative substitute	C	D7sus4	Em7	F sus2	G5	A m7	Dsus4/B
	Alternative bass note	C/E	Dm/F	Em/G	F/A	F/G	Am/E	

For all chords in the key of C# or Db, use the chords from the key of C with capo 1

GUITAR CHORDS

Roman	I	II	III	IV	V	VI	VII
Nashville	1	2	3	4	5	6	7

Key of D

	I	II	III	IV	V	VI	VII
3-note chord (triad)	D	Em	F#m	G	A	Bm	C#dim
4-note chord	Dmaj7	Em7	F#m7	Gmaj7	A7	Bm7	C#m7♭5
Alternative substitute	Dsus2	Em9	F#m7	G6sus2	A7sus4	Bm11	Aadd9/C#
Alternative bass note	D/F#	Em/B	F#m/A	G/B	G/A	Bm/F#	

For all chords in the key of D# or E♭, use the chords from the key of D with capo 1

Key of E

	I	II	III	IV	V	VI	VII
3-note chord (triad)	E	F#m	G#m	A	B	C#m	D#dim
4-note chord	Emaj7	F#m7	G#m7	Amaj7	B7	C#m7	D#m7♭5
Alternative substitute	E5	F#m11	G#madd♭6	Aadd9	Badd4	C#m7	D#alt
Alternative bass note	E/G#	F#m/C#	G#m/D#	A/C#	A/B	C#m/G#	

For all chords in the key of F, use the chords from the key of E with capo 1

For all chords in the key of F# or Gb, use the chords from the key of E with capo 2

172

GUITAR CHORDS

Roman	I	II	III	IV	V	VI	VII
Nashville	1	2	3	4	5	6	7

Key of G

3-note chord (triad)	G	Am	Bm	C	D	Em	F#dim
4-note chord	Gmaj7	Am7	Bm7	Cmaj7	D7	Em7	F#m7♭5
Alternative substitute	G	A7sus4	Dsus4/B	Cadd9	Dsus4	Em7	G/F#
Alternative bass note	G/D	Am/C	Bm/D	C/G	C/D	Em/G	

For all chords in the key of G# or A♭, use the chords from the key of G with capo 1

Key of A

3-note chord (Triad)	A	Bm	C#m	D	E	F#m	G#dim
4-note chord	Amaj7	Bm7	C#m7	Dmaj7	E7	F#m7	G#m7♭5
Alternative substitute	Asus2	Bsus4	C#m7	D6sus2	Eadd9	F#m11	Eadd9/G#
Alternative bass note	A/E	Bm/F#	C#m/E	D/A	D/E	F#m/A	

For all chords in the key of A# or Bb, use the chords from the key of A with capo 1

For all chords in the key of B, use the chords from the key of A with capo 2

173

SCRIPTURE INDEX

LUKE

1:37	You heal the broken hearted
4:18	We are free, the broken ones you have redeemed
4:18	You are matchless in grace and mercy
4:18	You give life
4:18	You heal the broken hearted
11:2	Oh we look to the Son
11:2	We are a flame that is burning bright
15:6	Amazing grace
15:24	Amazing grace
15:24	I once was lost, I walked away
19:10	I once was lost, I walked away
22:20	Once bound by fear, so lost in sin
23:33	I cast my mind to Calvary
23:33	There is a hill I cherish
24:6	From heaven to earth our Saviour came
24:6	On the cross you were broken

JOHN

1:1	You were the Word at the beginning
1:5	You give life
1:29	Behold this King so innocent
1:36	Behold this King so innocent
3:13	There is a God who has walked upon his earth
3:35	Jesus, name I can't forget
4:10	Are you thirsty?
4:10	Your love has led me to surrender
4:19	How sweet the name of Jesus sounds
5:26	You give life
6:31-33	How sweet the name of Jesus sounds
6:33	From heaven to earth our Saviour came
6:41	There is a God who has walked upon his earth
6:51	There is a God who has walked upon his earth
7:37-38	Are you thirsty?
9:1	Amazing grace
10:2	My life is a story bought by grace
10:11	How sweet the name of Jesus sounds
12:46	Hear our cry, oh King of heaven
14:6	How sweet the name of Jesus sounds
15:13	I once was lost, I walked away
15:13	Praise be to our God
15:13	You were the Word at the beginning
15:13-14	How sweet the name of Jesus sounds
16:20	How sweet the name of Jesus sounds
16:33	In this world we will face tribulation
16:33	O victory, you have won
16:33	On the cross you were broken
17:19	Come thou fount of every blessing
19:2	Behold this King so innocent
19:5	Behold this King so innocent
20:19-29	Listen to the words of the risen Christ

ACTS

2:25	God in the here and now
2:33	Father of kindness
2:33	He is alive
3:21	Spirit of God, come cleanse, renew
4:12	How sweet the name of Jesus sounds
4:12	Praise be to our God
22:16	One church, one faith, one anthem raised

ROMANS

3:24	My life is a story bought by grace
5:2	My life is a story bought by grace
5:3	In this world we will face tribulation
5:5	Father of kindness
5:8	Come thou fount of every blessing
5:8	I cast my mind to Calvary
6:4	Oh the thought, the wrath that I had earned
8:1-11	Christ was raised
8:22	We seek your kingdom
8:22	Your love so great, Jesus in all things
8:31	In this world we will face tribulation
8:31	You heal the broken hearted
8:34	Behold this King so innocent
8:35	Oh the thought, the wrath that I had earned
8:38	In this world we will face tribulation
8:38	You are matchless in grace and mercy
8:39	One church, one faith, one anthem raised
9:23	Father of kindness
10:9	We believe in one true God
10:9	We have hope for the coming days
10:13	How sweet the name of Jesus sounds
11:5	By grace I have been saved
11:27	All I have because of Jesus
12:1	O victory, you have won
12:21	There's nothing worth more
15:30	Oh the thought, the wrath that I had earned
16:25	He is alive

1 CORINTHIANS

1:17	On the cross you were broken
15:9	By grace I have been saved
15:12-28	Christ was raised
15:20	Behold this King so innocent
15:20	From heaven to earth our Saviour came
15:35-44	Christ was raised
15:54	Come, Lord Jesus, in your glory
15:54	O victory, you have won
15:58	Christ was raised

2 CORINTHIANS

1:3	Praise be to our God
1:20	Father of kindness
3:17	There's nothing worth more
4:9	He is alive
4:18	Oh we look to the Son
4:18	We fix our eyes on you, our Lord
7:4	In this world we will face tribulation
13:4	On the cross you were broken

GALATIANS

3:14	He is alive
4:7	You unravel me, with a melody
6:14	All I have because of Jesus
6:14	There is a hill I cherish

EPHESIANS

1:3	Praise be to our God
1:7	He lavishes grace as our burdens grow greater
1:10	Christ was raised
1:19-32	Christ was raised
2:1	Once bound by fear, so lost in sin
2:1-18	Christ was raised
2:4	Your love so great, Jesus in all things
2:5	Amazing grace
2:5	By grace I have been saved
2:6	Oh we look to the Son
2:7	He lavishes grace as our burdens grow greater
2:8	Amazing grace
2:8	My life is a story bought by grace
2:16	On the cross you were broken
3:8	You have called us out of darkest night
3:19	Oh the thought, the wrath that I had earned
3:20	Give me all eternity
3:20	The grace of God has reached for me

PHILIPPIANS

2:8	Oh the thought, the wrath that I had earned
2:8	On the cross you were broken
2:9	In this world we will face tribulation
2:10	He's coming on the clouds
2:10	O victory, you have won
2:10	One church, one faith, one anthem raised
2:10	Spirit of God, come cleanse, renew
2:10	We are a flame that is burning bright
2:6-11	From heaven to earth our Saviour came
2:6-11	We believe in one true God
2:6-11	We have hope for the coming days
3:8	There is a hill I cherish
4:7	My life is a story bought by grace

COLOSSIANS

1:17	We seek your kingdom
1:20	On the cross you were broken
2:13	Once bound by fear, so lost in sin
2:15	Christ was raised
3:2	Grander earth has quaked before

1 THESSALONIANS

4:14	We believe in one true God
4:14	We have hope for the coming days

2 THESSALONIANS

2:16	By grace I have been saved
2:16	My life is a story bought by grace
3:3	God the uncreated One

1 TIMOTHY

1:14	Father of kindness
3:14	Come, Lord Jesus, in your glory
3:16	Praise be to our God
4:8	He is alive
4:10	We have hope for the coming days
6:15	Can I walk the path less trodden?
6:15	God the uncreated One
6:16	From heaven to earth our Saviour came

2 TIMOTHY

3:7	Come thou fount of every blessing
3:10	He lavishes grace as our burdens grow greater

TITUS

3:4	I once was lost, I walked away
3:6	Father of kindness

HEBREWS

1:3	Behold this King so innocent
1:7	We are a flame that is burning bright
2:10	Come, Lord Jesus, in your glory
2:12	You have called us out of darkest night
4:3	Come, Lord Jesus, in your glory
4:14	How sweet the name of Jesus sounds
4:14-16	We have come to meet with you, O God
5:9	God the uncreated One
9:15	He is alive
10:23	We have hope for the coming days
11:1	We have hope for the coming days
12:2	Behold this King so innocent
12:2	Grander earth has quaked before
12:2	On the cross you were broken
12:13	Can I walk the path less trodden?
13:8	God in the here and now

JAMES

4:6	He lavishes grace as our burdens grow greater
4:7	Come, come as you are

1 PETER

1:3	Come thou fount of every blessing
1:3	O victory, you have won
1:3	Oh the thought, the wrath that I had earned
1:3	Praise be to our God
1:3	We fix our eyes on you, our Lord
1:7	He lavishes grace as our burdens grow greater
1:23	You unravel me, with a melody
2:4	In this world we will face tribulation
2:6	We fix our eyes on you, our Lord
2:9	Father of kindness
2:9	You have called us out of darkest night
2:25	Jesus, name I can't forget
5:5	He lavishes grace as our burdens grow greater

THEMATIC INDEX

for me
We believe in one true God
You give life
You heal the broken hearted
You unravel me, with a melody

GOD'S LOVE AND FAITHFULNESS

Are you thirsty?
By grace I have been saved
Come, come as you are
Come thou fount of ev'ry blessing
Even though I walk
Father of kindness
God in the here and now
He lavishes grace as our burdens grow greater
I once was lost, I walked away
In this world we will face tribulation
I've heard a thousand stories of what they think you're like
Jesus, name I can't forget
Let the King of my heart
My life is a story bought by grace
Oh the thought, the wrath that I had earned
On the cross you were broken
One church, one faith, one anthem raised
The grace of God has reached for me
There's nothing worth more
We are a flame that is burning bright
We have hope for the coming days
You are matchless in grace and mercy
You unravel me, with a melody
You who fear the Lord
Your love has led me to surrender
Your love so great, Jesus in all things

GUIDANCE AND DIRECTION

Come thou fount of ev'ry blessing
Jesus, name I can't forget

HEALING

Are you thirsty?
How sweet the name of Jesus sounds
There is a God who has walked upon his earth
Though the tears may fall my song will rise
We seek your kingdom
You are matchless in grace and mercy
You give life
You heal the broken hearted
You who fear the Lord

HEART WORSHIP

Behold this King so innocent
Can I walk the path less trodden?
From heaven to earth our Saviour came
Give me all eternity
God take us back, the place we began
God the uncreated One
How sweet the name of Jesus sounds
I cast my mind to Calvary
I've heard a thousand stories of what they think you're like
Let the King of my heart
My life is a story bought by grace
Praise be to our God
Spirit of God, come cleanse, renew
There is a God who has walked upon his earth
There is a hill I cherish
There's nothing worth more
Though the tears may fall my song will rise
We have come to meet with you, O God
You give life
You unravel me, with a melody
You were the Word at the beginning
Your love has led me to surrender

HEAVEN AND THE PROMISE OF ETERNITY

Amazing grace
Come, Lord Jesus, in your glory
God the uncreated One
He is alive
I cast my mind to Calvary
My hope is built on nothing less
Oh we look to the Son

The grace of God has reached for me
We have come to meet with you, O God

HOLY SPIRIT

Are you thirsty?
Can I walk the path less trodden?
God in the here and now
Spirit of God, come cleanse, renew
There's nothing worth more
We believe in one true God

JESUS - CROSS AND RESURRECTION

All I have because of Jesus
Amazing grace
Behold this King so innocent
Christ was raised
From heaven to earth our Saviour came
God the uncreated One
He is alive
I cast my mind to Calvary
Listen to the words of the risen Christ
Oh the thought, the wrath that I had earned
Praise be to our God
There is a hill I cherish
We believe in one true God
You were the Word at the beginning

JUSTICE

We seek your kingdom

LOVE AND DEVOTION

Can I walk the path less trodden?
Father of kindness
How sweet the name of Jesus sounds
I've heard a thousand stories of what they think you're like
Let the King of my heart
My life is a story bought by grace
There's nothing worth more
We fix our eyes on you, our Lord
We have come to meet with you, O God
You give life
You heal the broken hearted
Your love has led me to surrender
Your love so great, Jesus in all things

MERCY, GRACE AND FORGIVENESS

All I have because of Jesus

Amazing grace

Are you thirsty?

Behold this King so innocent

By grace I have been saved

Christ was raised

Come, come as you are

Hear our cry, oh King of heaven

I once was lost, I walked away

Jesus, name I can't forget

My life is a story bought by grace

Oh the thought, the wrath that I had earned

On the cross you were broken

The grace of God has reached for me

You were the Word at the beginning

MISSION

Listen to the words of the risen Christ

We are a flame that is burning bright

We seek your kingdom

You have called us out of darkest night

MYSTERY/ TRANSCENDENCE AND POWER OF GOD

By grace I have been saved

Christ was raised

Come, Lord Jesus, in your glory

From heaven to earth our Saviour came

Give me all eternity

God the uncreated One

Grander earth has quaked before

He's coming on the clouds

Hear our cry, oh King of heaven

Oh we look to the Son

Once bound by fear, so lost in sin

There is a God who has walked upon his earth

We have come to meet with you, O God

You heal the broken hearted

You were the Word at the beginning

Your love so great, Jesus in all things

PRAISE AND THANKSGIVING

Come thou fount of ev'ry blessing

Father of kindness

Give me all eternity

God the uncreated One

Hear our cry, oh King of heaven

How sweet the name of Jesus sounds

I cast my mind to Calvary

My life is a story bought by grace

On the cross you were broken

Once bound by fear, so lost in sin

One church, one faith, one anthem raised

Praise be to our God

The grace of God has reached for me

There is a God who has walked upon his earth

You give life

You have called us out of darkest night

Your love so great, Jesus in all things

PRAYER AND INTERCESSION

Can I walk the path less trodden?

Hear our cry, oh King of heaven

In this world we will face tribulation

I've heard a thousand stories of what they think you're like

We seek your kingdom

You who fear the Lord

PROCLAMATION

Christ was raised

From heaven to earth our Saviour came

God the uncreated One

He's coming on the clouds

Hear our cry, oh King of heaven

O victory, you have won

Oh we look to the Son

On the cross you were broken

Once bound by fear, so lost in sin

One church, one faith, one anthem raised

There is a God who has walked upon his earth

We believe in one true God

We have hope for the coming days

You are matchless in grace and mercy

You have called us out of darkest night

You heal the broken hearted

You were the Word at the beginning

Your love so great, Jesus in all things

RENEWAL AND REFRESHMENT

Are you thirsty?

Come, come as you are

Come, Lord Jesus, in your glory

He lavishes grace as our burdens grow greater

How sweet the name of Jesus sounds

There's nothing worth more

We fix our eyes on you, our Lord

You give life

You heal the broken hearted

You who fear the Lord

Your love has led me to surrender

RESPONSE

Can I walk the path less trodden?

Come, come as you are

Come, Lord Jesus, in your glory

God take us back, the place we began

Grander earth has quaked before

I once was lost, I walked away

Jesus, name I can't forget

Listen to the words of the risen Christ

My hope is built on nothing less

My life is a story bought by grace

Oh the thought, the wrath that I had earned

On the cross you were broken

Spirit of God, come cleanse, renew

The grace of God has reached for me

There is a hill I cherish

Though the tears may fall my song will rise

We fix our eyes on you, our Lord

We have come to meet with you, O God

We seek your kingdom

You unravel me, with a melody

Your love has led me to surrender

SPIRITUAL WARFARE

Even though I walk

God in the here and now

He is alive

He's coming on the clouds

O victory, you have won

The grace of God has reached for me

You are matchless in grace and mercy

You heal the broken hearted

You unravel me, with a melody

You were the Word at the beginning

SUFFERING AND TRIALS

Christ was raised

Come, come as you are

Even though I walk

God in the here and now

Grander earth has quaked before

He lavishes grace as our burdens grow greater

In this world we will face tribulation

My hope is built on nothing less

The grace of God has reached for me

Though the tears may fall my song will rise

We have hope for the coming days

You heal the broken hearted

You who fear the Lord

Your love has led me to surrender

TRINITY

He is alive

The grace of God has reached for me

There is a God who has walked upon his earth

We believe in one true God

We have hope for the coming days

You are matchless in grace and mercy

UNITY

Behold this King so innocent

In this world we will face tribulation

One church, one faith, one anthem raise

We are a flame that is burning bright

We believe in one true God

We have hope for the coming days

We seek your kingdom